Celebrate Piano!™

A Comprehensive Piano Method by
Cathy Albergo   J. Mitzi Kolar   Mark Mrozinski

LESSON AND MUSICIANSHIP 2B

National Library of Canada Cataloguing in Publication Data

Albergo, Cathy, 1951 –
      Celebrate piano : lesson and musicianship / Cathy Albergo, Jane Michelle Kolar,
Mark Mrozinski.

May be used in conjunction with Celebrate piano : solos.
Contents: Level 1A – level 1B – level 2A – level 2B – level 3 – level 4.
ISBN 0-88797-817-7 (level 1A). – ISBN 0-88797-819-3 (level 1B). –
ISBN 0-88797-843-6 (level 2A). – ISBN 0-88797-845-2 (level 2B). –
ISBN 0-88797-857-6 (level 3). – ISBN 0-88797-861-4 (level 4)

      1. Piano–Instruction and study–Juvenile. 2. Piano–Studies and
exercises–Juvenile. 3. Piano music–Teaching pieces–Juvenile. I. Kolar, Jane Michelle
II. Mrozinski, Mark III. Title.

MT746 A328 2003   j786.2'193'076   C2002-902826-4

FREDERICK
HARRIS
MUSIC

Table of Contents

Interval Safari Songs

Middle C Song

This is the sound of Mid - dle C.

2nds — **Busy Bee Song**

Bus - y bee, Bus - y bee, Bus - y Bus - y bum - ble bee.

3rds — **Cuckoo Bird Song**

Cuck - oo bird, Cuck - oo bird, Can you hear the Cuck - oo bird?

4ths — **Kangaroo Song**

Kan - ga - roo, Kan - ga - roo, Can I come and play with you?

5ths — **Owl Song**

"Hel - lo, hel - lo," says the lit - tle owl. "Hel - lo, hel - lo, stay with me a - while."

6ths — **Elephant Song**

LH over

El - e - phant, El - e - phant, he makes mu - sic with his trunk.

- 𝅘𝅥𝅮 𝅘𝅥.
- Major triads
- Crescendo, diminuendo
- Parallel and contrasting Answers

Practice Plan

➤ Tap HT and count.

➤ Play the different RH clusters in measures (mm.) 1, 9, and 13.

➤ Listen for accents, dynamics, and phrasing.

Rockin' Sunrise

With a beat

Mark Mrozinski

1-2   1

Teacher accompaniment. Student plays an octave higher.

Banjo and Cello—Imagine That! ▲

➤ Tap and ta the RH. Play and ta.

➤ Tap and ta the LH. Play legato and ta.

➤ Play HT.

➤ Transpose to the D♭ or E♭ Major 5-finger pattern.

Interval Safari

➤ Sing all the Interval Safari songs. See p. 3.

➤ Name the intervals your teacher or parent plays.

▲ staccato vs. legato

F26

A dot after a note lengthens the note by one half its value.

Dotted Quarter Discovery

➤ Tap and ta or count these rhythms.

➤ Write in the ta's or counts.

1

2

Practice Plan

➤ Circle the ♩. ♪ patterns. Tap and ta or count the rhythm.

➤ Name the RH notes in m. 7. What is the harmonic interval?

➤ Which hand plays F♯? F♮?

➤ Play the LH softer than the RH.

Exotic Birds

Key of _____

Grandly

Mark Mrozinski

3-4   2

Transpose

Transpose to the E Major 5-finger pattern. Warm up in the key first.

8va throughout

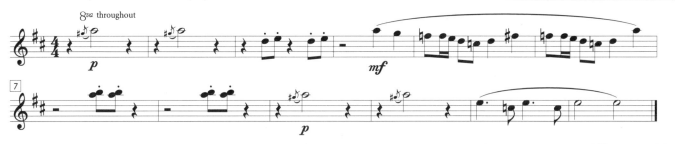

F

F25

A chord contains three or more notes. A chord with three notes is called a triad.

The Tonic (first), third, and fifth notes of a Major 5-finger pattern form a Major triad.

The Tonic, also called the Root, names the triad.

Tonic 3rd 5th
or
Root

5th
3rd
Tonic or Root

= C Major triad

Discovering Triads

➤ Name these triads.

➤ Play each triad.

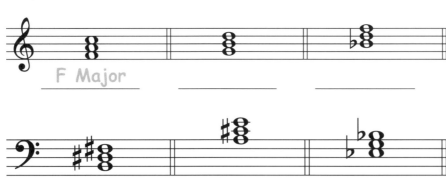

F Major _____ _____

_____ _____ _____

Broken and Blocked Triads

➤ Tap and ta.

➤ Warm up in the 5-finger pattern. Play and ta or count.

➤ Transpose to two new Major 5-finger patterns each day.

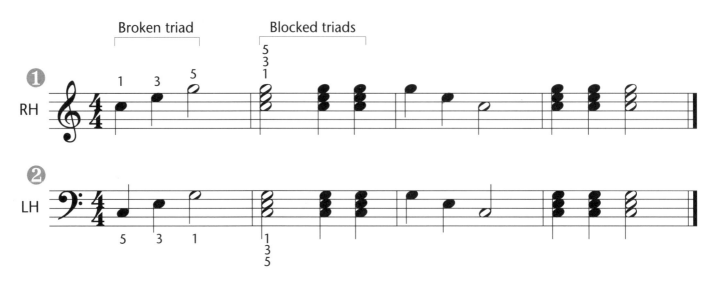

Broken triad   Blocked triads

❶
RH

❷
LH

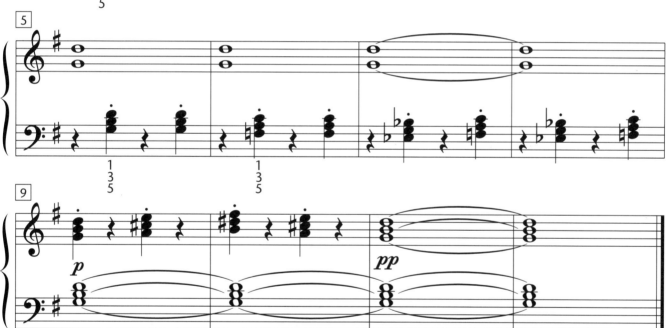

Practice Plan

➤ Tap HT and count. Did you remember the rests and ties?

➤ Name and play each Major triad.

➤ Practice moving quickly from one triad to the next.

Triadic Triumph

Key of _____

With spirit

Mark Mrozinski

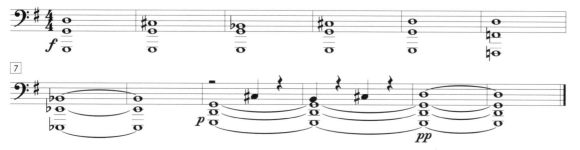

5-6   3

Teacher accompaniment. Student plays as written.

Practice Plan

➤ How do the dynamics tell the story of the parade?

➤ Tap HT and count.

➤ Block the hand positions in mm. 1-4 and 13-16.

➤ Name the Major triad.

crescendo (cresc.)

Play gradually louder.

diminuendo (dim.)

Play gradually softer.

The Parade

Key of _____

Marching

Here they come...

Mark Mrozinski

Student plays as written.

7-8   4

Teacher accompaniment

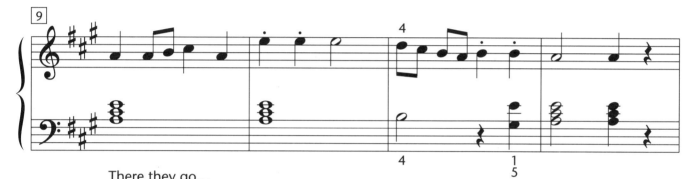

There they go…

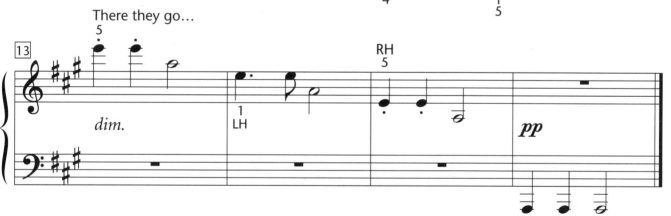

dim.

RH
5

LH

pp

5
LH

You Be the Judge!

Did you hear:
- *cresc.* and *dim.*?
- ♩. ♪ rhythm?
- steady beat?
- LH softer than RH in mm. 5-12?

Rainbow Leaps ▲

➤ Play finger 1 on Middle C, then leap to the next C in the shape of a rainbow.

➤ Repeat on other keys.

RH   1 leap up to 5

LH   1 leap down to 5

Triple Treat

➤ To write each triad:

1. Play the 5-finger pattern.

2. Write the Tonic.

3. Complete the triad using line–line–line or space–space–space. Remember to add sharps or flats if needed.

C Major   D Major   F♯ Major   A♭ Major

F Major   A Major   D♭ Major   E♭ Major

▲ octave

Coded Message

To break the code:

➤ Write the Magic Formula for the Major 5-finger patterns:

   <u>Keynote</u> <u>W</u> <u>___</u> <u>___</u> <u>___</u>

➤ Write the missing finger numbers for each pattern.

➤ Write the name and play each pattern.

❶ = <u>C</u>

❷ = _____

❸ = _____

❹ = _____

❺ = _____

❻ = _____

❼ = _____

❽ = _____

❾ = _____

❿ = _____

Message

➤ Fill in the blanks with the names of the 5-finger patterns
to complete the hidden message.

<u>C</u> __ n you __in__ th__ k__ys? __ __ sh__rp! __♭on't __♭__♭ fl__♭t!
❶❷   ❸   ❹   ❺   ❻   ❺❻   ❷   ❼   ❽❾   ❿

⑨ Pitch Detective

Listen as your teacher plays a four-note pattern of quarter notes beginning on Middle C, using 2nds, 3rds, 4ths, or 5ths.

➤ Play what you hear.
➤ Write the pattern on the staff.

❶

❷

❸

⑨ Echo Game—Clapbacks!

Listen as your teacher claps a rhythmic pattern.
➤ Echo or clap what you hear!

⑨ Echo Game—Playbacks!

Listen as your teacher plays a melodic pattern.
➤ Play the melody that you hear in the
D♭ Major 5-finger pattern.

Clapbacks:

Playbacks:

cresc.

dim.

Parallel and Contrasting Answers

A parallel Answer begins the same as the Question.

A contrasting Answer begins differently from the Question.

Both parallel and contrasting Answers end on the Tonic.

Question and Answer

➤ Play this parallel Question and Answer.

➤ Play this contrasting Question and Answer.

➤ Play this Question and create both a parallel and a contrasting Answer.

➤ Write your favorite Answer.

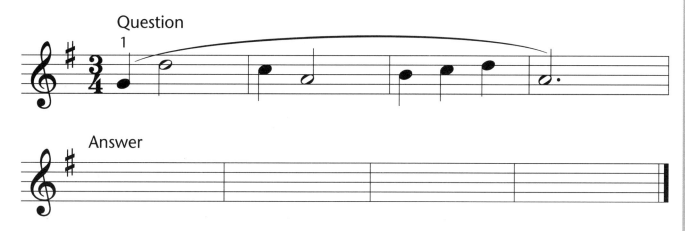

Practice Plan

➤ Name and play the blocked and broken triads.

➤ Tap and ta the RH melody in mm. 3-10. Discover the two-measure rhythmic pattern and its variations.

➤ Write the counts in mm. 4, 6, and 8.

The Hound Dawg Song

Key of _____

With energy

Folk song

9-10   5

Teacher accompaniment. Student plays as written.

The Hound Dawg Song is an Ozark mountain song from before the Civil War. The melody is based on the old fiddler's tune "Sally Anne."

7

Makes no dif-f'rence if he is a hound. They got-ta stop chas-in' my

10

dawg a - round.

p

ff

Transpose

Transpose to the A Major 5-finger pattern. Warm up in the key first.

- Interval: octave
- ⌢
- Key signatures: flat keys

5-finger Warm-ups

➤ Tap and ta each exercise.

➤ Transpose to two or more 5-finger patterns each day. Keep a firm, rounded hand position.

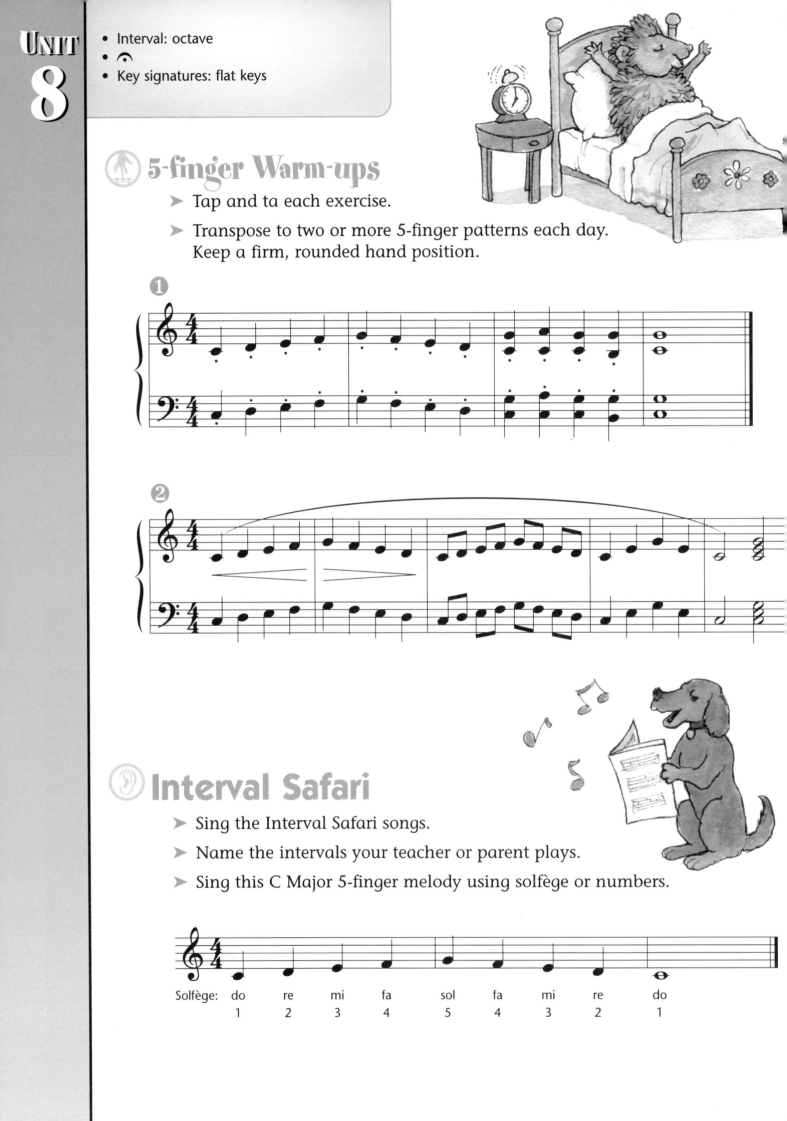

Interval Safari

➤ Sing the Interval Safari songs.

➤ Name the intervals your teacher or parent plays.

➤ Sing this C Major 5-finger melody using solfège or numbers.

Solfège:	do	re	mi	fa	sol	fa	mi	re	do
	1	2	3	4	5	4	3	2	1

An octave is the distance from a note to the next note of the same letter name.

From C to the next C, up or down, is an octave; from D to the next D, up or down, is an octave.

An octave skips from a space to a line, or a line to a space.

Discovering Octaves

F27

➤ Draw each octave.

➤ Name and play each octave.

Interval Safari: Donkey Song

The **Donkey Song** uses octaves.

➤ Sing and play the **Donkey Song**.

➤ Make sure you are singing in tune.

Hee - haw, hee - haw, don - keys are smart. Hee - haw, hee - haw, right from the start.

Practice Plan

➤ Practice **Octave Challenge** on p. 21.

➤ Tap HT and count.

➤ Find and practice the octaves in mm. 7, 8, and 12.

➤ Name the Tonic and Dominant in the LH.

➤ Play the LH accompaniment softer than the RH melody.

Fermata

⌢ Hold the note longer than its value.

Alouette

Key of _____

French Folk song

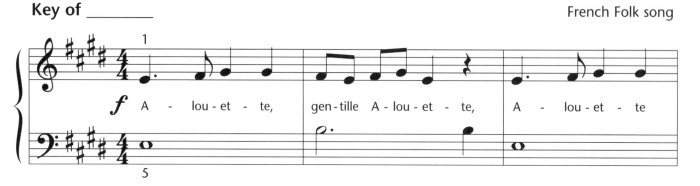

A - lou - et - te, gen - tille A - lou - et - te, A - lou - et - te

je t'y plu - me - rai. *cresc.* Je t'y plu - me - rai la tête, *dim.* je t'y plu - me - rai la tête,

Et la tête, Et la tête, A - lou - ette, A - lou - ette, O... O...

17-18   9

Teacher accompaniment. Student plays one octave higher.

Alouette is a song about a bird whose feathers are plucked from different parts of its body in each verse. This song is always sung in French, with different parts of the body added for each verse:

Je t'y plumerai le tête (*I will pluck them off your head*)
Je t'y plumerai les yeux (*I will pluck them off your eyes*)
Je t'y plumerai le nez (*I will pluck them off your nose*)

English words:
Alouette, pretty Alouette,
I will pluck your feathers all away.
Alouette, pretty Alouette,
I will pluck your feathers all away.
I will pluck them off your head, I will pluck them
off your head.
Off your head, Off your head, Alouette, Alouette, Oh!

Octave Challenge

➤ Warm up in the key. Name the Tonic and Dominant.

➤ Play the octaves in the shape of a rainbow.

➤ Transpose to C and E Major.

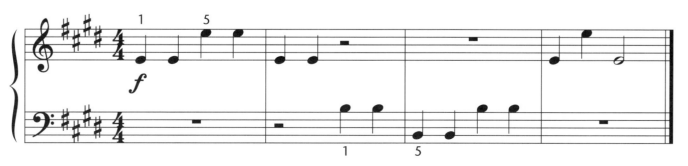

Practice Plan

➤ Block and name the triads in mm. 1-6.

➤ Practice mm. 5-8 separately.
What are the LH positions?

Journey of the Triads

Key of _____

Walking along

Mark Mrozinski

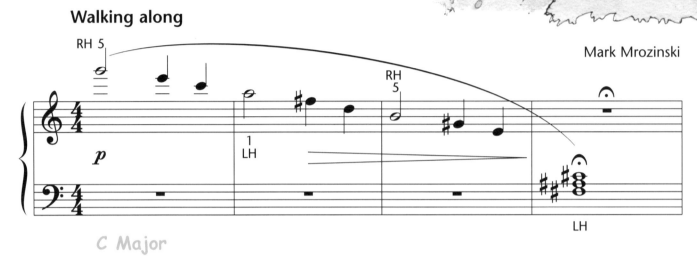

C Major

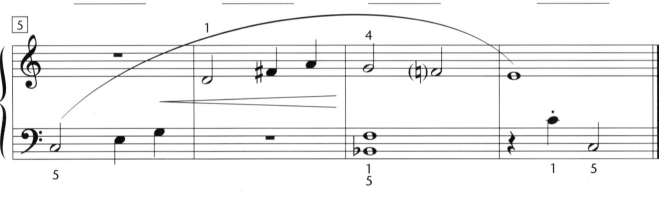

➤ Using the rhythm of **Journey of the Triads**,
make up your own triad piece.

Title: _____

**You Be
the Judge!**
Did you hear:
• _dim._ and _cresc._?
• 𝄐 ?
• legato phrases?

19-20   10

Teacher accompaniment. Student plays as written.

Flats are always written on both Treble and Bass staffs in the same order: B E A D G C F. This is the order of the sharps backwards.

In flat keys, the next to the last flat in the key signature names the key.

F Major has only one flat.

Discovering Flat Key Signatures

➤ Circle the next to last flat.

➤ Write the name of the key.

F28

Key of _C♭ Major_

Key of _____

Key of _____

Key of _____

Key of _____

Key of _____

Key of _____

Practice Plan

➤ Tap HT and count.

➤ Find patterns that are the same or similar.

➤ Practice mm. 1-8 HS and HT. Repeat for mm. 9-16.

➤ Name and play the LH interval between mm. 8 and 9.

➤ Name and play the LH triad.

Donkey Riding

Canadian Folk song

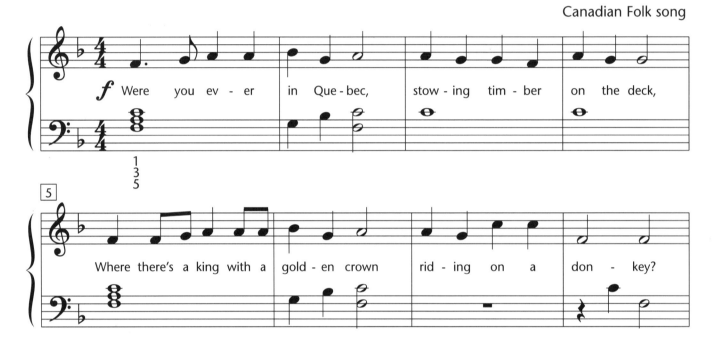

f Were you ev - er | in Que - bec, | stow - ing tim - ber | on the deck,

1
3
5

5 Where there's a king with a | gold - en crown | rid - ing on a | don - key?

21-22   11

Teacher accompaniment. Student plays one octave higher.

mf

9

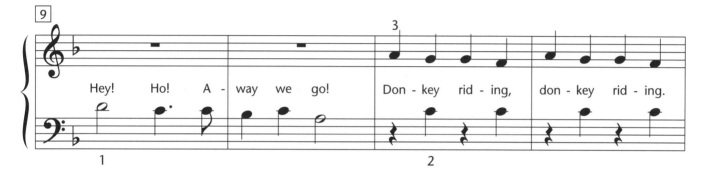

What's a Donkey?

Donkey Riding was a work song for sailors. The "donkey" was the machine that pulled the ropes on lumber boats.

9

Hey! Ho! A - way we go! Don - key rid - ing, don - key rid - ing.

13

Hey! Ho! A - way we go! Rid - ing on a don - key.

Practice Plan

➤ Warm up in the key, using staccato.

➤ Tap HT and count.

➤ Play HS to discover the repeated patterns.

➤ What makes mm. 11-14 easy to play?

Leaky Faucet

Key of _____

With a steady drip

Mark Mrozinski

23-24   12

Teacher accompaniment. Student plays as written.

8va throughout

pp *sempre staccato*

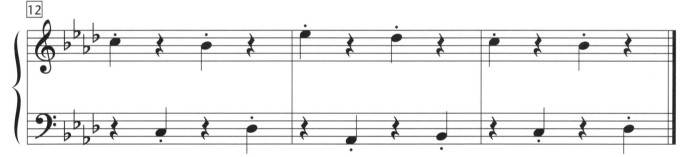

➤ Play **Leaky Faucet** again, slowing down in the last two measures.▲

Transpose

Choose a key and transpose **Leaky Faucet**.

➤ Make up your own **Leaky Faucet** piece in the E♭ Major 5-finger pattern using the accompaniment pattern below.

➤ Does your faucet have a fast or slow drip?

▲ *rit.*

Practice Plan

Write your own **Practice Plan**.

➤ _____

➤ _____

➤ _____

➤ _____

Jumping Jacks

Key of _____

With a bounce

Susan Alcon

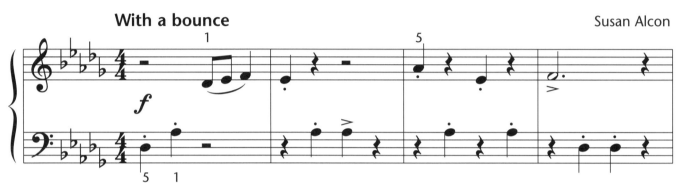

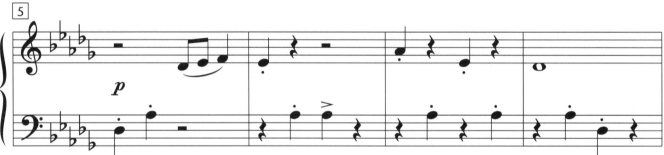

25-26   13

Tracing Flats

➤ Trace each flat in order (B, E, A, D, G, C, F).
➤ Draw the seven flats in order on the blank staff.

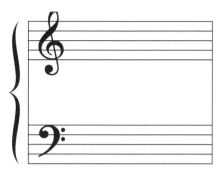

Key Signature Challenge

➤ For each example, draw the key signature on the Treble staff and Bass staff. Place each flat clearly in a space or on a line.

1
➤ Draw one flat.
➤ Name the key.

Key of _____

2
➤ Draw two flats.
➤ Name the key.

Key of _____

3
➤ Draw four flats.
➤ Name the key.

Key of _____

Polka Dotted Quarters

➤ Play the melody as written.

➤ Play it again, changing to the ♩. ♪ rhythm where shown.

➤ Repeat, changing to the ♩. ♪ rhythm in a different measure.

Rechargeable Batteries ▲

➤ Clap and ta the rhythm.

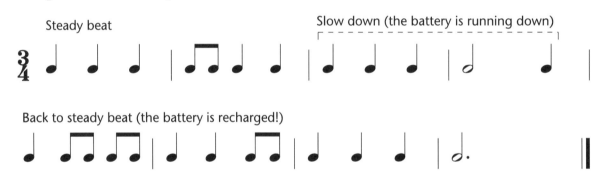

Charged-up Melody

➤ Using the rhythm above, create your own RH melody in the E♭ Major 5-finger pattern.

➤ Create another melody using your LH in the B♭ Major 5-finger pattern.

▲ *rit.; a tempo*

Mystery Melody

➤ Complete this familiar folk song by playing the melody and writing the missing notes for each ✖.

➤ Clap and ta.

➤ Name this melody.

Title: _____

Echo Game–Clapbacks!

Listen as your teacher claps a rhythmic pattern.

➤ Echo or clap what you hear!

Echo Game–Playbacks!

Listen as your teacher plays a melodic pattern.

➤ Play the melody that you hear in the Eb Major 5-finger pattern.

- Ostinato
- Ritardando
- Tempo and *a tempo*

🎠 Balancing Act ▲

➤ Name the key.

➤ Identify the fingers that play together.

➤ Play HT and listen carefully for legato RH and staccato LH.

➤ Transpose to one new key each day.

👂 Interval Safari

➤ Sing the Interval Safari songs for 2nds, 3rds, 4ths, 5ths, 6ths, and octaves.

➤ Name the intervals your teacher or parent plays.

➤ Sing this C Major 5-finger melody using solfège or numbers.

do	re	mi	fa	sol	fa	mi	re	do
1	2	3	4	5	4	3	2	1

▲ legato vs. staccato

An ostinato is an accompaniment pattern that repeats.

Practice Plan

➤ Tap HT and count.

➤ Where is the ostinato pattern? Practice the pattern.

➤ Play HT, listening for legato and staccato.

Russian Dance

Delicately, not too fast

Stephen Chatman

33-34   17

Teacher accompaniment. Student plays one octave higher.

Mark Mrozinski

Practice Plan

➤ _____

➤ _____

➤ _____

➤ _____

Once a Canadian Lad

This song describes the feelings of a 19th-century Canadian rebel who is sent to the United States.

He stops by a stream that flows towards Canada and asks it to carry his sad greetings to his friends at home.

Once a Canadian Lad

Key of _____

Canadian Folk song

f Once a Ca - na - dian lad, ex - iled from

hearth and home, Walked in a for - eign land,

35-36   18

Teacher accompaniment. Student plays one octave higher.

mf con pedale

a tempo

rit.

Tempo

The speed of a piece is called the tempo.

ritardando (*rit.*)	Gradually slow down.
a tempo	Return to your original tempo.

Transpose

Transpose to F Major.

You Be the Judge!

Did you hear:
* *rit.* and *a tempo*?
* ties?
* 𝄐 ?
* LH softer than RH?

Practice Plan

➤ Tap HT and count.

➤ Find and play the ostinato.

➤ Where is the hesitation?

Hesitation Hop

Key of _____

Lively

Mark Mrozinski

37-38   19

Transpose

Transpose to B Major or C Major.

Teacher accompaniment. Student plays one octave higher.

Practice Plan

➤ Name the LH intervals and find the ostinato.

➤ Where does the ostinato change position? Name the lowest note.

➤ Where does the RH move to the C Major position? Where does the RH play E♭?

➤ Practice the measures you found most challenging.

Last Train to Bluesville

Key of _____

Steady beat

Mark Mrozinski

39-40   20

Teacher accompaniment. Student plays as written.

Crosswalk ▴

➤ Name the two notes played by finger 2 in each hand.

➤ Play, crossing finger 2 over finger 1. Let finger 2 walk over the thumb without twisting your wrist.

❶

❷

Mix 'n' Match Triads

➤ Draw a line connecting each triad to its Tonic.

➤ Play each triad.

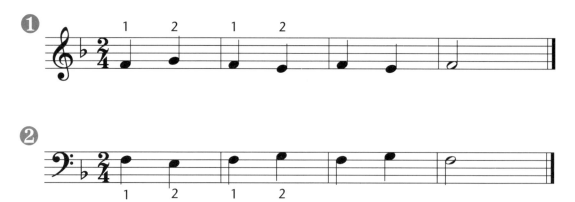

B

F♯

G

D♭

E

B♭

▴ finger crossing

Leaping Letters ▲

➤ Name the first note in each example.

➤ Follow the directions to write two more notes.

➤ Name the last note.

❶

<u>C</u> ↑8   ↓2 <u>B</u>

❷

___ ↑8   ↓2 ___

❸
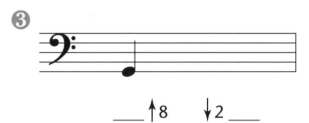

___ ↑8   ↓2 ___

❹
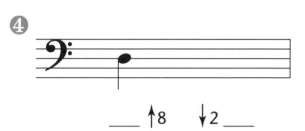

___ ↑8   ↓2 ___

Keys to Success

➤ Draw each key signature and name the key.

➤ Play the Major 5-finger pattern for each key.

Draw 3 flats
in each staff

Key of _____

Draw 3 sharps
in each staff

Key of _____

Draw 6 sharps
in each staff

Key of _____

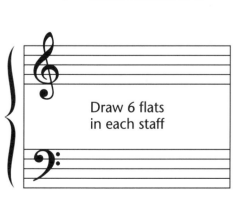

Draw 6 flats
in each staff

Key of _____

▲ 7ths

UNIT 9

Tapping Together

➤ Tap the RH, the LH, then HT.

Challenge: Choose any two notes and play the examples.

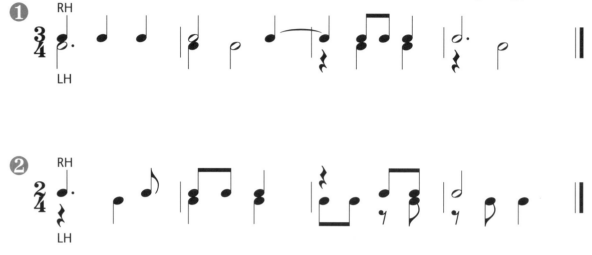

Pattern Detective

Listen as your teacher plays one of the patterns in each example.

➤ Point to the pattern your teacher plays.

➤ Play each pattern yourself.

Question and Answer

➤ Create several parallel and contrasting Answers to this Question. Be sure to end on the Tonic.

➤ Write your favorite Answer.

Question

Answer

Echo Game–Clapbacks! ▲

Listen as your teacher claps a rhythmic pattern.

➤ Echo or clap what you hear!

Echo Game–Playbacks!

Listen as your teacher plays a melodic pattern.

➤ Play the melody that you hear in the B Major 5-finger pattern.

Next Stop Bluesville

➤ Using the LH pattern from **Last Train to Bluesville** (p. 37), create your own RH melody using the C Major 5-finger pattern plus E♭.

Clapbacks:

Playbacks:

dim.

▲ ♪ upbeat

• Interval: 7th
• Form: AB, ABA
• *D.C. al Fine*

Tumbling Triads

➤ Name the key, and the Tonic and Dominant.

➤ Where do you play legato? staccato?

➤ Where are the broken triads? the blocked triads?

➤ Transpose to one new key each day.

Interval Safari

➤ Sing the Interval Safari songs.

➤ Name the intervals your teacher or parent plays.

➤ Sing this C Major 5-finger melody using solfège or numbers.

do	re	mi	fa	sol	fa	mi	re	do	mi	sol	mi	do
1	2	3	4	5	4	3	2	1	3	5	3	1

Interval: 7th

7ths skip: from a space to a space
from a line to a line

Count: 7 lines and spaces

F **Discovering 7ths**

F29

➤ Draw each 7th.

➤ Name both notes and play the 7th.

_D_ ↑7 _C_

___ ↓7 ___

___ ↓7 ___

___ ↓7 ___

___ ↑7 ___

___ ↑7 ___

Interval Safari: Giraffe Song

The **Giraffe Song** uses 7ths.

➤ Sing the **Giraffe Song**.

➤ To find the 7th, play up an octave to Treble C and down a 2nd.
Make sure you are singing in tune.

Reach-ing up high, in - to the trees, Ger - ry Gir - affe, eat-ing the leaves.

Rainbow 7ths

➤ Tap and ta or count.

➤ Play the 7ths in the shape of a rainbow.

➤ Play **Rainbow 7ths**. Be sure to move your hand to the
F Major pattern (hand position) in mm. 2 and 4.

➤ Transpose to C Major.

F Major hand position

F Major hand position

Teacher accompaniment for **Graceful Swan**. Student plays one octave higher.

Practice Plan

➤ Circle the RH 7ths and practice mm. 1-4.

➤ Find the change to the F Major hand position in mm. 4 and 11. Practice moving in rhythm. (You may need to look quickly at your hand on beat 2.)

➤ Find and practice the LH patterns.

Graceful Swan

Key of _____

Gliding smoothly

Mark Mrozinski

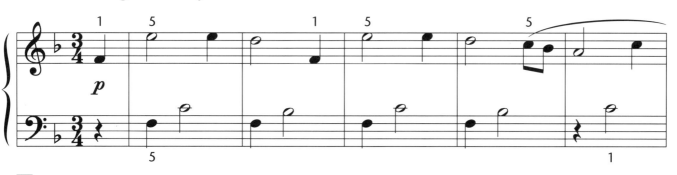

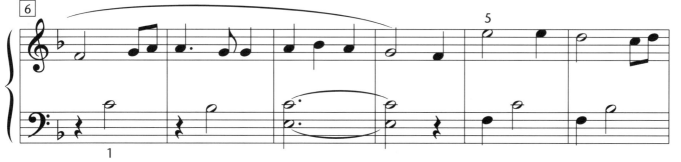

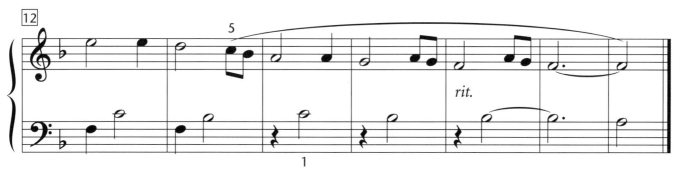

You Be the Judge!

Did you hear:
- phrases?
- *rit.*?
- softer accompaniment?

43-44   22

Form: AB and ABA

A piece of music often has more than one section. Sections may be the same or different. The order of these sections is called form.

AB form has two sections that are different.
ABA form has three sections. The first and third sections are the same. The second section is different.

Fun Form Friends

➤ Look at these pictures. Are they in AB or ABA form?

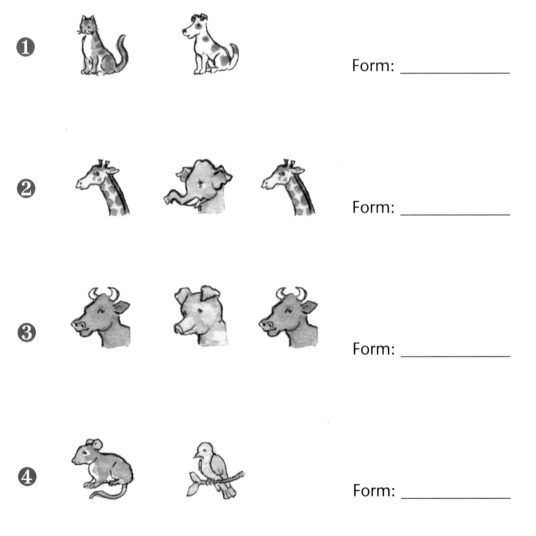

1   Form: _____

2   Form: _____

3   Form: _____

4   Form: _____

5 Find the A and B sections in **Yodeler's Holiday**.

Practice Plan

➤ Tap HT and count.

➤ Find and play two different 5ths in the LH. Practice moving between the LH 5ths without looking at your hand!

➤ In the B section, circle the octaves and box the 7ths. Rainbow play these intervals.

D.C. al Fine

D.C. al Fine = Da Capo al Fine
Go back to the beginning (*Da Capo*) and play to the end (*Fine*).

Yodeler's Holiday

A Section

Form: ABA

Merrily

Mark Mrozinski

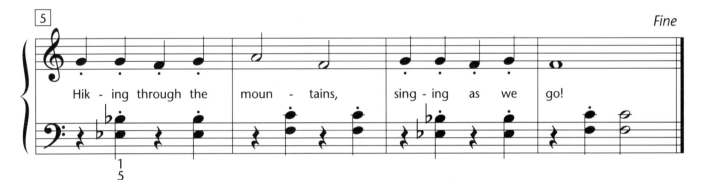

B Section

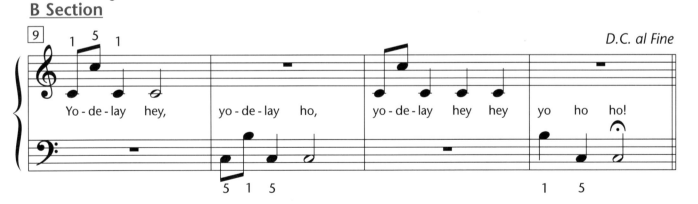

45-46   23

Teacher accompaniment. Student plays as written.

Practice Plan

➤ Tap HT and count.

➤ Label the A and B sections. What is the form?

➤ In the A section, circle and play the melodic and harmonic 6ths.

➤ Practice mm. 17-24 HT with the correct fingering.

Mexican Dance

Key of _____

Circle the form:
AB ABA

With spice

Mark Mrozinski

47-48   24

Teacher accompaniment. Student plays one octave higher.

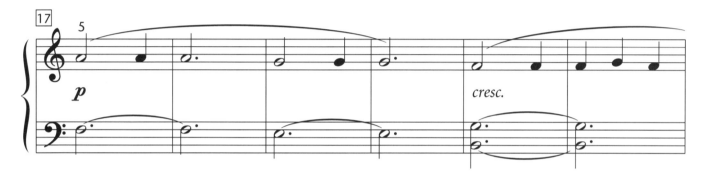

Transpose

Transpose the
<u>A Section</u> to F Major.

Practice Plan

➤ Identify the form and label the A and B sections.

➤ Which hand begins the melody? Where does the melody change hands?

➤ Place a ✔ over each RH position change. Practice each move.

➤ Identify and play each LH 5th and 6th.

Polly Wolly Doodle

Key of _____

Circle the form:
AB   ABA

Folk song

49-50   25

Teacher accompaniment. Student plays as written.

13

goin' to Lou'-si-an-a for to | see my Su-si-an-na, Sing | Pol-ly Wol-ly Doo-dle all | day.

Verse 2

My Sal she is a maiden fair,
Sing Polly Wolly Doodle all day.
With curly eyes and laughing hair,
Sing Polly Wolly Doodle all day.
Fare thee well…

Verse 3

Oh a grasshopper sitting on a railroad track,
Sing Polly Wolly Doodle all day.
Pickin' his teeth with a carpet tack,
Sing Polly Wolly Doodle all day.
Fare thee well…

Transpose

Play the RH of **Polly Wolly Doodle** in the C or G Major 5-finger pattern.

Doodling Polly

➤ Circle one note in each line of **Polly Wolly Doodle**.

➤ Choose another note from the F Major 5-finger pattern to replace each circled note.

➤ Play your variation of **Polly** with a steady beat.

➤ Try other variations.

Crisscross Fingers ▴

➤ Find and circle each place finger 2 crosses over finger 1.

➤ Play on the keyboard cover.

➤ Play with a rounded hand position. Repeat, crossing with finger 3 instead of 2.

Interval Mix-up

➤ Name these notes and melodic intervals.

➤ Play the intervals.

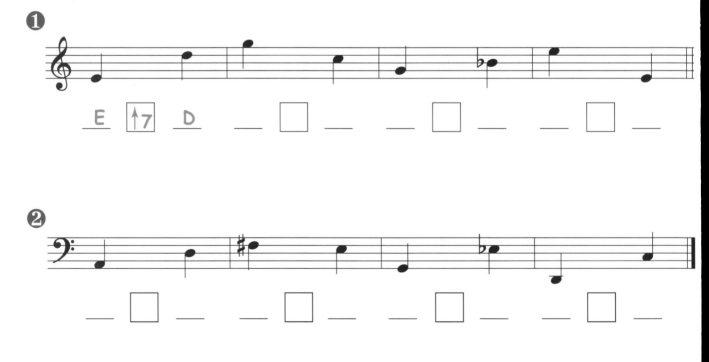

▴ finger crossing

Terrific Triads

For each example:

➤ Play the 5-finger pattern and triad.

➤ Write the triad, using sharps or flats if needed.

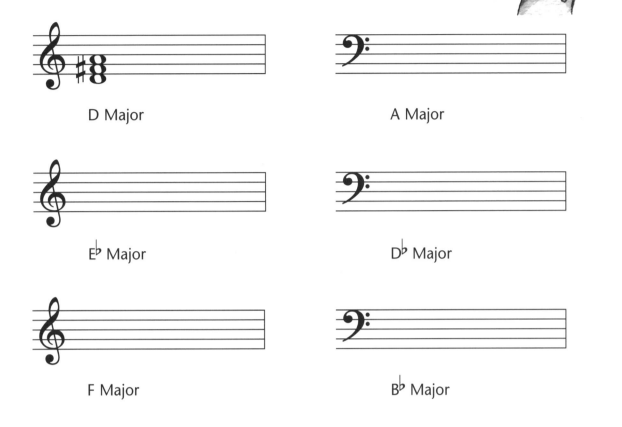

D Major

A Major

E♭ Major

D♭ Major

F Major

B♭ Major

Rhythm Math Game

➤ Tap and count each example.

➤ How many beats are in each box? Write the number of beats in the circle.

➤ Add the numbers in the circles to find the answer.

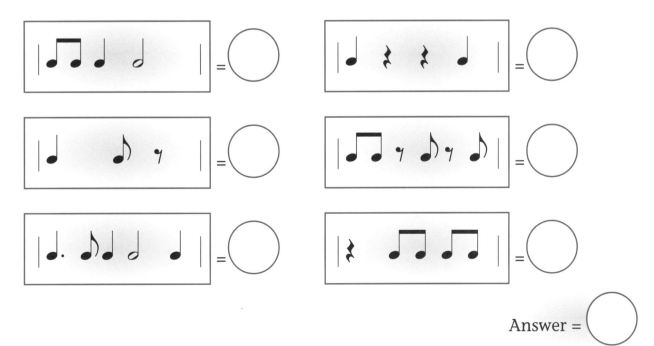

Answer = ◯

Math Game answer: 22

Writing the Rhythm

Listen as your teacher plays a rhythmic pattern.

➤ Clap and ta the pattern.

➤ Write the pattern.

❶

$\frac{4}{4}$

❷

$\frac{3}{4}$

Yodeler's Solo

➤ Create your own four-measure B section for **Yodeler's Holiday** (see p. 47). Use octaves and 7ths to create your yodel.

➤ Play **Yodeler's Holiday** with your new B section.

Echo Game–Clapbacks! ▲

Listen as your teacher claps a rhythmic pattern.

➤ Echo or clap what you hear!

Echo Game–Playbacks!

Listen as your teacher plays a melodic pattern.

➤ Play the melody that you hear in the B♭ Major 5-finger pattern.

Clapbacks:

Playbacks:

▲ ♪ upbeat

NIT

11

- Finger crossing
- Introduction
- ♪ upbeat
- 8va
- Coda

5-finger Warm-up ▲

➤ Name the key, and the Tonic and Dominant.

➤ Play legato and then staccato.

➤ Transpose to one new key each day.

Interval Safari

➤ Sing the Interval Safari songs for 2nds, 3rds, 4ths,
5ths, 6ths, 7ths, and octaves.

➤ Name the intervals your teacher or parent plays.

➤ Sing this C Major 5-finger melody using solfège or numbers.

do	re	mi	fa	sol	fa	mi	re	do	mi	sol	mi	do
1	2	3	4	5	4	3	2	1	3	5	3	1

▲ I and V⁷

Practice Plan

➤ Circle each time RH finger 2 crosses over the thumb.

➤ Find the *rit.*, fermata, and *a tempo*.

➤ Find and play the melodic 6th.

An introduction is a short section of the piece that comes before the **A Section**.

Popcorn Man

Introduction   A Section

With a snap   Mark Mrozinski

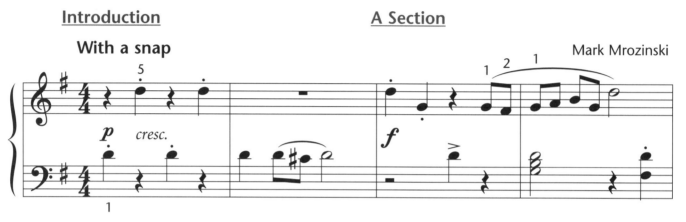

57-58   29

Teacher accompaniment. Student plays one octave higher.

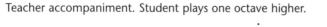

You Be the Judge!

Did you hear:
- dynamics?
- accents?
- staccatos?

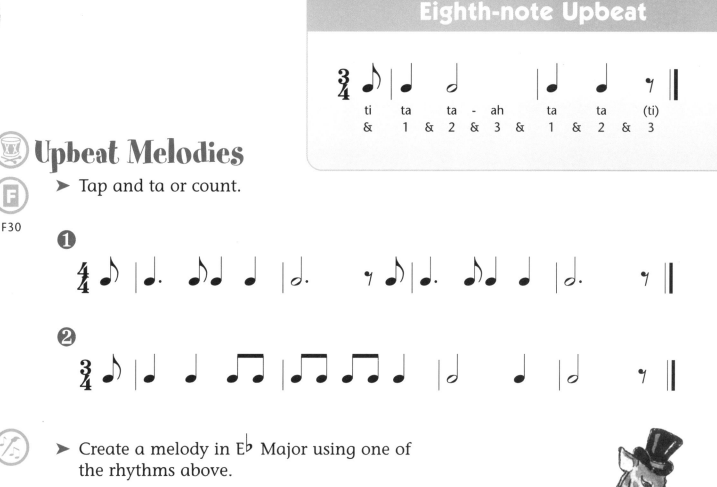

ti ta ta - ah   ta   ta (ti)
&   1 & 2 & 3 & 1 & 2 & 3

Upbeat Melodies

➤ Tap and ta or count.

F30

1

2

➤ Create a melody in E♭ Major using one of the rhythms above.

➤ Accompany your melody with 5ths or 6ths in the LH. Listen carefully to choose the interval that sounds best.

Easy Over

➤ Name the finger numbers as you play this exercise on the keyboard cover.

➤ Circle each note played by finger 2 in either hand. Did you cross over using a half step or a whole step?

➤ Play **Easy Over** keeping a rounded hand position.

➤ Transpose to F or C Major.

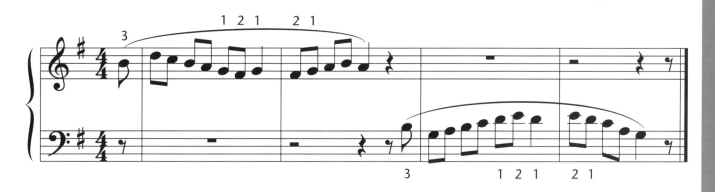

Practice Plan

➤ Circle the eighth-note upbeat.

➤ Where does the piece end?

➤ Where do you play legato?

➤ Count carefully in m. 16 before returning to the A Section.

Play an octave higher.

March of the Bugs

Key of _____

Circle the form:
AB   ABA

Allegro

Mark Mrozinski

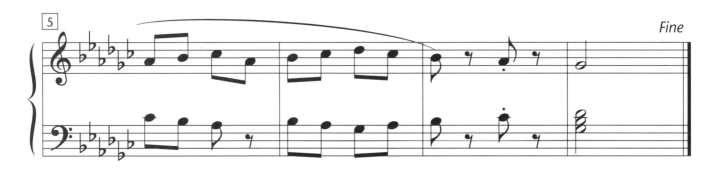

5

1

5

Fine

59-60   30

Teacher accompaniment. Student plays as written.

mf

Fine

9

pp

D.C. al Fine

rit.

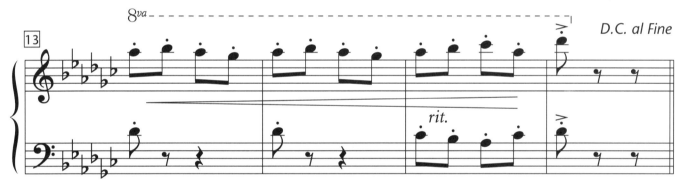

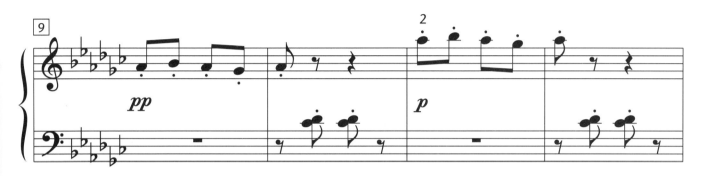

D.C. al Fine

Transpose

Transpose to A Major.

Practice Plan

➤ Compare mm. 1-8 with mm. 9-16 and 25-32. How are they the same? different?

➤ Find the repeat signs. What do you repeat?

Repeat

Music between two repeat signs should be played twice.

Melodious Exercise

op. 149, no. 3

Anton Diabelli
(1781–1858)

Key of _____

61-62   31

Teacher accompaniment. Student plays as written.

Anton Diabelli

Diabelli was an Austrian music publisher who taught piano and guitar. He composed a number of piano pieces as well as sacred music, dance music, and songs.

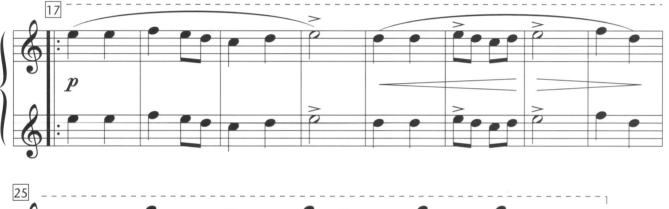

Transpose

Transpose to E Major.

Practice Plan

➤ How does your hand position change to play the coda? Practice this move.

➤ Play the LH 5ths blocked then broken.

➤ Circle and play the LH harmonic 6ths.

Coda

A coda is an ending section added to the form. In Italian, coda means tail.

Sea Chanty

Key of _____

Circle the form:
AB ABA

Mark Mrozinski

Rolling

Heave ho! the old an - chor and raise up the sails! We

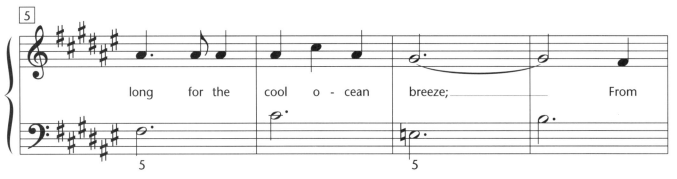

long for the cool o - cean breeze; From

63-64   32

Teacher accompaniment. Student plays one octave higher.

Chanty

A chanty is a work song for sailors as they raise the sails, pull the ropes, or lift the anchor.

dawn   'til   dusk   we   haul   the   ropes   and

Coda

head   for   the   o   -   pen   seas.

p

It's a Match ▲

Match these key signatures and triads.

➤ Draw a line connecting the key signature to the correct triad.

➤ Name the Tonic and Dominant.

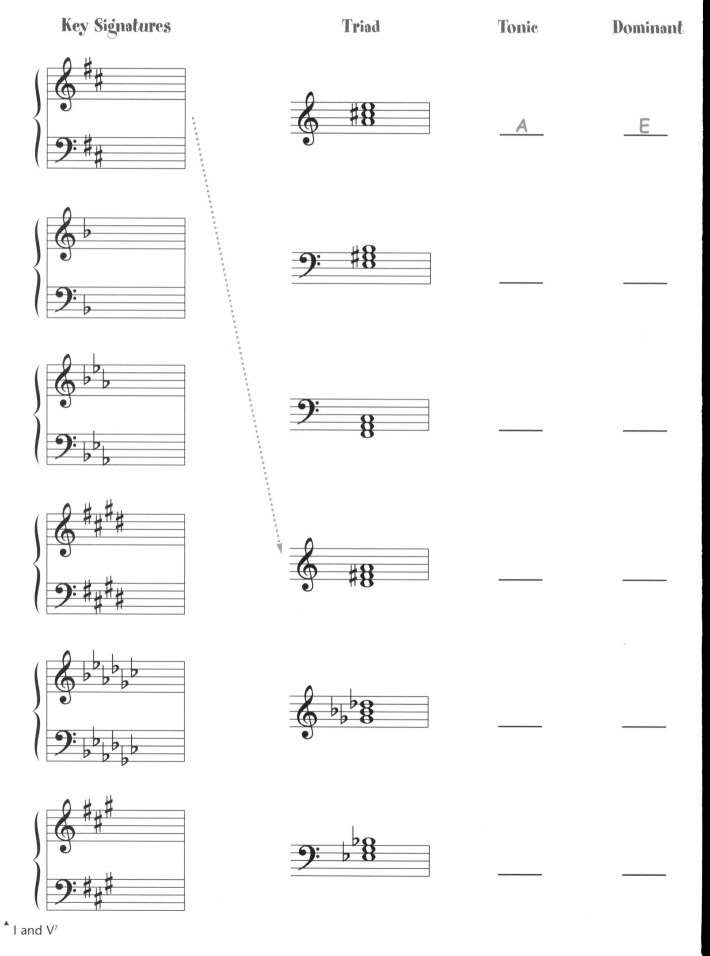

Key Signatures	Triad	Tonic	Dominant
		A	E

▲ I and V⁷

Name that Tune

➤ Discover the name of the mystery tune by completing these clues. One piece in this book contains all of the items listed as clues.

➤ Name the mystery tune.

Clues

1 Write an F Major triad.

2 Write a key signature with one flat.

3 Name the key of Clue No. 2.

———————————

4 Circle the sign meaning loud.

p   *f*

5 Name this interval.

6 Name the notes of the F Major 5-finger pattern.

7 Write the one rest that will replace **o**.

8 Write the Tonic and Dominant from Clue No. 6.

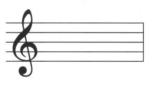

9 Tap and ta this rhythm.

10 Write the time signature of Clue No. 9.

Mystery tune: ———————————————

What's Missing?

➤ Fill in the missing note or rest above each ✖.

➤ Clap and ta or count the rhythm.

Mystery Melody

➤ Complete this familiar folk song by playing the melody and writing the missing notes for each ✖.

➤ Clap and ta.

➤ Name this melody.

Title: _____

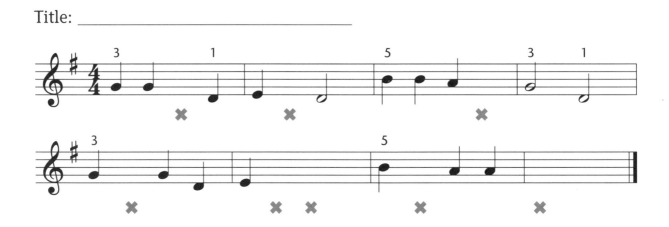

Question and Answer

➤ Create several parallel and contrasting Answers to this
   Question. Be sure to end on the Tonic.

➤ Write your favorite Answer.

Question

Answer

Echo Game–Clapbacks! ▲

Listen as your teacher claps a rhythmic pattern.

➤ Echo or clap what you hear!

Echo Game–Playbacks!

Listen as your teacher plays a melodic pattern.

➤ Play the melody that you hear in the
   A♭ Major 5-finger pattern.

Clapbacks:

Playbacks:

▲ $\frac{6}{8}$

🏃 5-finger Climb ▲

➤ Play this 5-finger exercise in C Major, then move up one half step to D♭ Major and play again.

➤ Name the Tonic and Dominant for each key.

➤ Keep moving up by half steps to play new keys. How high did you climb?

👂 Interval Safari

➤ Sing all the Interval Safari songs.

➤ Name the intervals your teacher or parent plays.

➤ Sing this C Major 5-finger melody using solfège or numbers.

▲ I and V⁷

Hidden Triads

For each example:

➤ Complete the Major triad by using two notes from the **Note Bank**. Only one Major triad is possible.

➤ Play each triad.

Note Bank   **Major Triads**

1

2
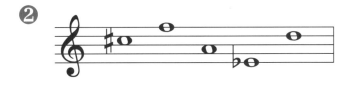

3

4

5

Practice Plan

➤ What is the time signature?

➤ Compare the LH rhythm in mm. 1-6 with mm. 9-14. Play and ta these rhythms.

➤ Which two notes does finger 1 play? Practice this move.

Skip to My Lou

Key of _____

Circle the form:
AB ABA

Folk song

Skip,   skip,   skip   to my Lou.   Skip,   skip,   skip   to my Lou.

Fine

Skip,   skip,   skip   to my Lou.   Skip   to my Lou, my   dar - ling.

69-70   35

Teacher accompaniment. Student plays one octave higher.

mf
LH detached

Fine

D.C. al Fine

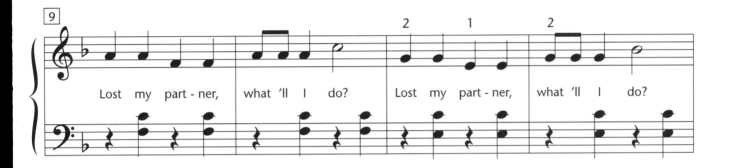

9

Lost my part - ner, what 'll I do? Lost my part - ner, what 'll I do?

D.C. al Fine

13

Lost my part - ner, what 'll I do? Skip to my Lou, my dar - ling.

Transpose

Transpose to E♭ Major and A♭ Major.

🎵 Skip to My Lou Variation

➤ Create a variation by changing one or more notes in each line of the RH. Create a new variation each time you play.

Practice Plan

➤ Find and play the LH ostinato pattern. How does this pattern change in mm. 7-8?

➤ Write a ✔ under each RH or LH finger 2 crossover. Practice these separately.

➤ Circle each F♮. Practice the RH phrases.

Desert Caravan

Key of _____

Slowly swaying

Mark Mrozinski

71-72   36

Dynamics: *mf* and *mp*

mf   mezzo forte = medium loud

mp   mezzo piano = medium soft

ff   fortissimo = very loud

f   forte = loud

mf   mezzo forte = medium loud

mp   mezzo piano = medium soft

p   piano = soft

pp   pianissimo = very soft

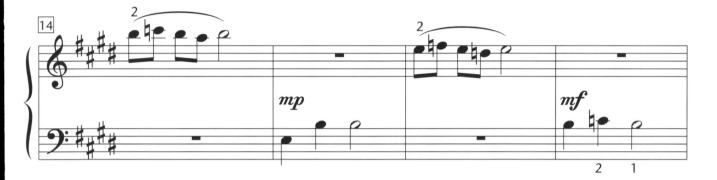

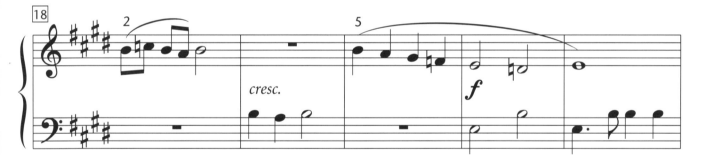

You Be the Judge!

Did you hear:

- *cresc.* and *dim.*?
- *rit.*?
- legato phrases?

Practice Plan

➤ How is the LH different in mm. 1 and 2? Practice this change.

➤ Place a ✔ under each RH finger 2 crossover. Is there a LH crossover?

➤ Warm up in the key before you play.

Riding the Waves

Key of _____

Circle the form:
AB ABA

Mark Mrozinski

Sailing

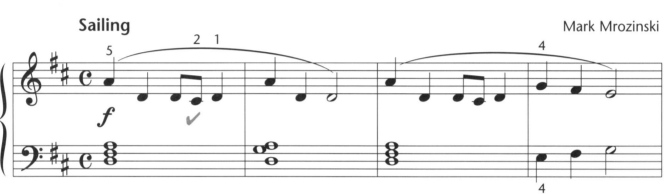

73-74   37

Teacher accompaniment. Student plays one octave higher.

D.C. al Fine

Transpose

Transpose to E and G Major.

Over the Top

➤ Circle the crossovers. Notice that the LH finger 2 crosses over by a whole step. The RH finger 2 crosses over by a half step.

➤ Play.

➤ Transpose this exercise to C, D, E, G, A, or B Major?

Time Signature Workout

➤ Write the correct time signature.

➤ Clap and ta or count the rhythm.

➤ Which example could be in Common Time **C** ? _____

❶

❷

❸

Musical Crossword

➤ Read each clue and write the answer in the correct squares
on the puzzle.

Across
1. The distance between two notes
3. Gradually slower
4. Gradually louder
10. Names the key of a piece
12. A chord with 3 notes
14. Lowers a note one half step
16. Fifth note in a Major 5-finger pattern
17. Interval: C up to B
18. Play short and detached

Down
2. Cancels a sharp or flat
5. Gradually softer
6. Pick-up
7. Interval: F to F
8. Hold the note longer than usual
9. Smooth and connected
11. Raises a note one half step
13. Return to the original tempo
15. First note in a Major 5-finger pattern

Pitch Detective

Listen as your teacher plays a four-note pattern starting on G.

➤ Play what you hear.
➤ Write the pattern on the staff.

❶

❷

Echo Game–Clapbacks! ▲

Listen as your teacher claps a rhythmic pattern.

➤ Echo or clap what you hear!

Echo Game–Playbacks!

Listen as your teacher plays a melodic pattern.

➤ Play the melody that you hear in the
D Major 5-finger pattern.

Question and Answer

➤ Warm up in the key.
➤ Create your own Question ending on the Dominant.
➤ Create a parallel or contrasting Answer ending on the Tonic.

Question

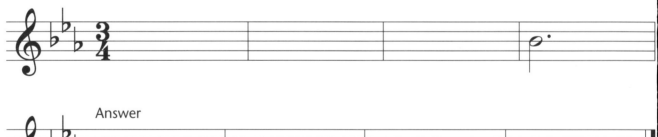

Answer

Clapbacks:

Playbacks:

▲ 6/8

Rhythm Ace

Key of _____

Circle the form:
AB ABA

Mark Mrozinski

75-76 38

Congratulations!

You have completed **Celebrate Piano!**™ **Level 2B**
and are now ready for **Celebrate Piano!**™ **Level 3**.

Cathy Albergo   *J. Mitzi Kolar*   *Mark Mrozinski*

Teacher   Date